Topz

Christmas Cracker

Alexa Tewkesbury

CWR

Published 2013 by CWR, Waverley Abbey House, Waverley Lane,
Farnham, Surrey GU9 8EP, UK. Registered Charity No. 294387.
Registered Limited Company No. 1990308.

See back of book for list of National Distributors.

Concept development, editing, design and production by CWR
Printed in the UK by Page Brothers
ISBN: 978-1-85345-993-1

Hi! We're the Topz Gang

– Topz because we all live at the 'top' of something …
either in houses at the top of the hill, at the top of the
flats by the park, even sleeping in a top bunk counts!
We are all Christians, and we go to Holly Hill School.

We love Jesus, and try to work out our faith in God
in everything we do – at home, at school and with
our friends. That means trying to show God's love
(especially at Christmas!) to the Dixons Gang who
tend to be bullies, and can be a real pain!

If you'd like to know more about us, visit our website
at **www.cwr.org.uk/topz** You can read all about us,
and how you can get to know and understand the Bible
more by reading our *Topz* notes, which are great fun,
and written every two months just for you!

My name is:

_____

and this Christmas book is ALL MINE!

This is what I look like wearing a Father Christmas hat
(draw yourself wearing a Father Christmas hat here):

This is what my house looks like wearing a Father Christmas hat (draw your house wearing a Father Christmas hat here):

Christmas Topz 10

I LOVE Christmas! It's my absolute favourite time of year! I get so excited, I can't sleep! My twin brother John's just the same. Sometimes we text each other in the middle of the night on Christmas Eve, just to see if we're still awake – and we usually are! Here's a list of the five things I love MOST about Christmas time. What about you? If you can add five of YOUR favourite things about Christmas, we'll have a Christmas Topz ten!

1. Advent calendars! Come on – chocolate every morning for 24 days?? Scrumptious!

2. Christmas shopping! I love choosing presents for my family and friends.

3. Decorating the Christmas tree! The fun starts here!

4. Making Christmas cards. Josie and I sometimes make them together. I like using glitter but it makes a bit of a mess. Oops …

5. Saying 'Happy Birthday' to Jesus on Christmas morning! After all, without Jesus, there wouldn't be Christmas!

Your turn! What do **YOU** love best about Christmas?

6.

7.

8.

9.

10.

Mad About Christmas Food!

When it comes to food, I know what I like! And when it comes to CHRISTMAS food, I know what I like and most of the time I get to eat it, too! My ideal Christmas Day meal menu would be:

Breakfast: Scrambled egg on toast followed by a mince pie.

Lunch: Roast potatoes, roast parsnips, carrots and peas, with LOADS of gravy, all topped off with masses of melty grated cheese (I know – I'm very weird!). Pudding would of course be Christmas pudding – but the ice cream version (yes, there is one!).

Supper: Toast and Marmite, peanuts and a piece of Christmas cake (or maybe two pieces, because my mum's Christmas cake is SOOO good!).

Write down YOUR ideal Christmas Day meal menu here:

Breakfast

_____

_____

Lunch

_____

_____

Supper

_____

_____

These are some of the different foods that people traditionally eat at Christmas:

Yule log	Cranberry sauce	Christmas pudding
Satsumas	Roast potatoes	Mince pies
Chestnuts	Brussels sprouts	Turkey
Parsnips	Stuffing	Dates

Can you find them in the word search?

T	U	R	K	E	Y	J	E	J	D	T	G	F	U	M	L
Z	S	Y	S	E	O	T	A	T	O	P	T	S	A	O	R
W	R	Q	H	B	V	F	G	N	I	F	F	U	T	S	U
W	C	R	O	S	T	U	N	T	S	E	H	C	P	Z	N
C	R	A	N	B	E	R	R	Y	S	A	U	C	E	W	W
D	T	S	J	S	C	S	A	T	S	U	M	A	S	T	I
G	I	E	T	V	D	E	L	S	P	I	N	S	R	A	P
F	H	T	N	D	I	G	O	L	E	L	U	Y	X	S	N
B	K	A	Z	F	L	O	P	F	C	O	K	D	G	Y	C
H	X	D	J	T	S	E	I	P	E	C	N	I	M	R	J
G	N	I	D	D	U	P	S	A	M	T	S	I	R	H	C
B	R	U	S	S	E	L	S	S	P	R	O	U	T	S	G

Benny's mum puts lots of yummy things into her Christmas cake. Here are a few of her special ingredients, plus something that shouldn't be there. Cross it out if you know what it is:

Currants	Cinnamon	Sultanas	Mustard
Raisins	Brown sugar	Eggs	Flour

Answers on page 109

How Well Do You Know the Christmas Story (Part 1)?

Dave and Danny have made up a quiz for you so that you can test your knowledge. You'll find all the answers in the Bible – the Christmas story as told by Luke in the New Testament (chapter 1, verses 26 to 38, and chapter 2, verses 1 to 20). First, why not see how many questions you can answer WITHOUT having to look them up in the Bible. (You'll also find the answers on page 109.)

1. Where did Mary live?

N _____

2. Whom did God send to Mary with a message?

G _____

3. God wanted Mary to be afraid of Him.

True or false? _____

4. Mary was engaged to a man called Joseph. Joseph was a descendant of which king?

K_____   **D**_____

5. Where did Mary and Joseph have to go for the census? (A census is a count of numbers of people.)

B _____

6. When they arrived, where did Mary and Joseph stay?

In a _____

7. After Jesus was born, who were the first people God invited to see His baby Son?

s _____

8. The shepherds believed what the angels told them about the baby Jesus.

True or false? _____

9. What did the angels do after one of them had announced the birth of Jesus?

They s_____ p_____ to God.

10 The shepherds went to Bethlehem but there was no sign of the baby Jesus.

True or false? _____

Answers on page 109

11

Present Time!

Christmas is a fantastic time for making our friends and family happy with the presents we give them. If you could give a present to each of the Topz Gang, what would you choose?

Draw your gift next to the appropriate Gang member.

My 'Before' and 'After' Christmas Lists

What's on YOUR Christmas wish list? If you're reading this book BEFORE Christmas, write down some of the presents you'd love to receive here:

_____

_____

_____

_____

Were you given what you hoped for? If you're reading this book AFTER Christmas, write down your favourite Christmas presents here:

_____

_____

_____

_____

_____

Arty Time!

One of Sarah's Topz five favourite things about Christmas is decorating the tree. Here's a tree ready and waiting for lots of festive festooning. Colour it, glitter it, stick things to it! How funky can you make it for Christmas?

Decorations Galore!

Here are just some of the things you might find hanging on Christmas trees over the festive season:

Baubles   Lights   Tinsel
Fairies   Ribbon bows   Candy canes
Angels   Bells   Chocolates
Stars

See if you can track them all down in the word search:

P	I	L	S	U	I	B	M	D	C	S
F	S	E	L	B	U	A	B	A	L	W
F	L	S	L	K	X	D	N	B	C	O
A	I	N	E	C	S	D	E	S	F	B
I	G	I	B	T	Y	M	L	Q	M	N
R	H	T	A	C	H	E	V	D	F	O
I	T	R	A	E	G	Z	G	G	I	B
E	S	N	V	N	E	I	K	Q	F	B
S	E	T	A	L	O	C	O	H	C	I
S	U	Q	A	L	G	Z	H	L	U	R

Answer on page 109

Is there anything else hanging on your Christmas tree? If so, write it here:

A Stylish Way to Say
THANK YOU!

Now that the arty side of your brain is all warmed up, why not have a go at creating some fabulous and completely original notepaper? You can give it a Christmas theme and use it to write 'thank you' letters to your friends and family for the lovely presents they've given to you. Sending emails is fine, but everyone loves to receive a letter now and again – especially when it's written on super-stylish paper with your own special twist!

DESIGN IDEAS:

- On the left-hand half of the paper, draw and decorate a Christmas tree like the one on page 14. You can then write your 'thank you' letter on the blank, right-hand half.

- Cut out different small shapes from Christmas wrapping paper – for example, stars, square 'present' shapes, mini-Christmas trees, bells – and stick them around all four edges of your piece of paper to create a colourful and Christmassy border.

- Make your border by drawing instead of sticking. Think of something Christmassy – for example, a holly leaf, a mini angel, a Christmas star – and draw lots of them around the four edges of your piece of paper. Then colour them in. You can either keep to one image per piece of paper, or you can mix them up.

Here's some space for you to practise your designs. Try cutting out a few wrapping paper shapes and laying them side by side to see what looks good with what. And have a go at drawing some ideas for your notepaper borders. Mix and match your Christmas images until you've come up with something really special!

How Well Do You Know the Christmas Story (Part 2)?

More questions from Dave and Danny about Christmas. This time they've looked in the New Testament at the book of Matthew, chapter 2 and verses 1 to 15. Do you know the answers without looking in the Bible first?

1. Where did the wise men who wanted to visit Jesus come from?

☐ The north ☐ The south

☐ The east ☐ The west

2. Where did the wise men find King Herod?

☐ In a stable ☐ In Jerusalem ☐ In Bethlehem

3. What did the wise men ask when they reached King Herod's court?

☐ 'When is Jesus' birthday?'

☐ 'What can we give Jesus as a present?'

☐ 'Where is the baby born to be the King of the Jews?'

4. Whom did King Herod ask where Jesus was to be born?

☐ The chief priests and the teachers of the Law

☐ The queen ☐ His mum

5. What did King Herod ask the wise men to do when they found Jesus?

☐ Wish Jesus a very happy birthday

☐ Tell him where Jesus was

☐ Congratulate Mary and Joseph on the new baby

6. What stopped over the place where Jesus was?

☐ A bird ☐ The moon ☐ A star

7. Why didn't the wise men go back to King Herod on their way home?

☐ They got lost ☐ God told them not to

☐ They forgot

8. Where did Joseph take Jesus and Mary to keep them safe from King Herod?

☐ To Egypt ☐ To his parents' house

☐ Back home to Nazareth

Answers on page 109

Could You Report on a Big Story? (1)

Paul's been thinking about what it might have been like to be a reporter for a newspaper around the time of the birth of Jesus. He's imagined that he works for a paper called *The Daily Lamp*, and he's been sent to get the BIG STORY: the Son of God being born in a stable on the very first Christmas.

Here's the report Paul's written for his paper:

In the very early hours of the morning (far too early for me to be up!) something amazing seems to have happened in Bethlehem. The town was apparently packed out with people who'd turned up to be counted in the census, and unless you had a room booked you didn't stand a chance of getting a place to stay.

But for one innkeeper, whose inn was already full to the eyeballs, finding space for two more guests wasn't a problem. 'The man asked me if I had a room for him and his wife, and I knew I couldn't turn them away', he told me. 'His wife was about to have a baby – and when I say "about to", I mean *about to*! I showed them round to my stable and said they could spend the night there. And before too long, the little 'un was born!'

From all accounts, this baby is no ordinary child. There have been reports of strange lights in the sky over the town, and of the sounds of singing. Shepherds who came to visit the new baby confirmed that the singing was from a sky full of angels. One angel in particular had told them that this baby was the Son of God.

Now it's YOUR turn! You've been given the chance to scoop the BIGGEST news story in the history of the world!

Give the newspaper you work for a name:

If you look at the front page of several different newspapers, you'll notice that all the paper names are designed differently. If Paul's newspaper was real, the name on the front page might look like this:

Now that you've given YOUR newspaper a name, create a design for it here:

Could You Report on a Big Story? (2)

For his report, Paul decided to interview the Bethlehem innkeeper who let Mary and Joseph stay in his stable. You could talk to him, too, if you like, or to any of the others who played a part in the first Christmas.

Here's a list of everyone involved. Think carefully about what each one might be able to tell you and how what they say could make your report as interesting and exciting as possible. Then tick the people you'd most like to talk to. It can be as many as you want.

☐ The innkeeper

☐ Mary

☐ Joseph

☐ The shepherds

☐ King Herod

☐ The wise men

☐ One of the angels

Now you know who you want to talk to, it's time to start planning your interviews. You're going to need to come up with some good questions to find out all you can about what happened on that first Christmas. (And obviously, as you're imagining this report the way Paul did, you'll have to come up with some brilliant answers, too, based on what you know from the Bible!)

When you've thought of some questions, use the space below to note them down. You could write in brackets after each one the name of the person you want to ask that particular question. You could also jot down brief answers, which will help you when you come to write up your report.

Could You Report on a Big Story? (3)

This is it! You've done all your investigating! You've asked your questions and got hold of some really interesting answers! Now it's time to WRITE YOUR REPORT! See if you can use all your interviews – there's plenty of writing space – and link them together in an interesting way. Why not look back at Paul's report and read through it again to help you get started.

_____

_____

_____

_____

_____

_____

_____

_____

_____

_____

_____

_____

_____

_____

_____

_____

_____

_____

Report brought to you by (your name):

_____

Could You Report on a Big Story? (4)

Wow! Your news report is mega-stonkingly brilliant! It's definitely going to be your newspaper's front cover story! What you need now is a really catchy headline to make everyone want to read it. Here's the headline I made up for mine. Write yours underneath in big blocky letters the way I've done – just like you see on the front of newspapers!

Baby's birth causes BIG stir in Bethlehem

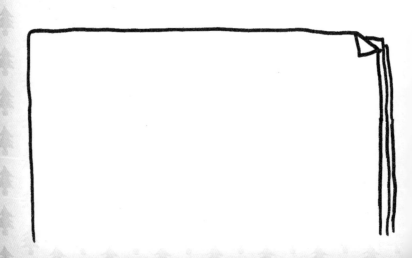

And finally ...

Every GREAT newspaper story has a GREAT picture to go with it. Here's a picture of the scene in the stable on that very first Christmas night. Colour it in to make it really eye-catching for your readers!

Can't wait to grab a copy of your newspaper!

Topz' Cool Christmas Quiz

1. Holly is often used as a decoration at Christmas. What colour are its berries?

☐ blue   ☐ red   ☐ green

2a. Do the twelve days of Christmas begin before or after Christmas Day?

_____

2b. What are the dates of the twelve days?

_____

3. What do we call the days of December that lead up to Christmas Day?

_____

4. Who told Mary to name God's Son, 'Jesus'?

_____

5. What is the name of the Church festival that starts after Christmas to celebrate the visit of the wise men to Jesus?

_____

6. How many days are there in December, the Christmas month?

☐ 28   ☐ 30   ☐ 31

7. You can read all about the birth of Jesus in the New Testament in the Bible. Does the Old Testament mention it, too?

☐ Yes   ☐ No

8. Along with holly, mistletoe is another plant that people sometimes hang up to decorate their homes at Christmas. What colour are mistletoe berries?

☐ white   ☐ orange   ☐ purple

9. Three wise men travelled a long way in search of the young Jesus. They each had a present for Him. What were their presents – and can you spell them correctly? The first one is easy!

G _ _ _   F _ _ _ _ _ _ _ _ _ _   M _ _ _ _

10. The shepherds and the wise men were thrilled to hear that Jesus had been born. Why was King Herod angry about it?

_____

_____

Answers on page 109

Which is which?

It's not always just tinsel and baubles that are used as Christmas decorations. Lots of people decorate their homes with greenery and plants, too.

Here are five plants that we traditionally associate with Christmas:

A Mistletoe   **B** Ivy   **C** Christmas Rose

D Poinsettia   **E** Holly

Do you know which is which? Match each picture with its plant name by writing the correct letter next to it.

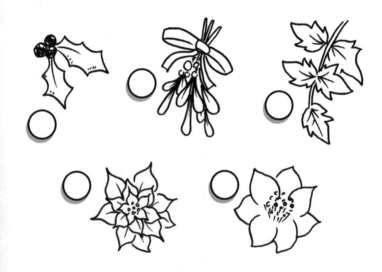

Answers on page 109

Rockin' Robins

If someone asked you to name the bird you most associate with Christmas, you'd probably say, 'A robin!' Christmas cards are full of pictures of these gorgeous little birds with their bright red breasts.

But did you know …?

- … that in Britain, robins are just about the only birds you might hear singing on Christmas Day. It would be nice to think that they were joining in with the Christmas fun, but actually they sing for a different reason. It's to let other robins know that this is their territory – the place where they live. They're not keen on sharing their home with any other robins either, so really their song is another way of saying: 'This is MY bit! Keep out!'

- … that a robin doesn't start life with a red breast. Its baby feathers are brown and speckly. The red ones don't begin to appear until the robin is two to three months old.

- … that way back in 1960, robins became even more special. They were given the great honour of becoming the national bird of Britain.

How Well Do You Know Your Christmas Carols?

I love singing Christmas carols! Sometimes Topz go carol-singing around Holly Hill to collect money for a charity. And at our school carol concert at the end of term, I even played my violin! Have a look below at the first lines of some of my favourite carols. Can you fill in the missing words?

1. The holly and the __ __ __

2. Once in __ __ __ __ __ David's city

3. O little __ __ __ __ of Bethlehem

4. In the bleak __ __ __ __ __ __ __ __ __

5. The first __ __ __ __ __ __ the __ __ __ __ __ did say

6. __ __ __ __ in a manger

7. While __ __ __ __ __ __ __ __ __ __ watched their

__ __ __ __ __ __ by night

8. __ __ __ __ __ __ night, holy night

9. O come all ye __ __ __ __ __ __ __ __ __

10. Hark! The __ __ __ __ __ __ __ angels sing

Answers on page 110

Now look at the word search. How quickly can you find all twelve of those words from Christmas carols?

R	S	D	L	A	R	E	H	P	O
S	E	P	W	V	F	H	R	B	Q
Q	H	T	F	T	U	P	O	T	F
U	X	E	N	L	Y	R	Y	O	G
A	R	Z	P	I	O	Q	A	W	A
Y	V	P	G	H	W	C	L	N	N
B	A	B	S	C	E	D	K	L	G
N	O	W	E	L	L	R	I	S	E
P	Q	X	A	I	V	Y	D	M	L
L	U	F	H	T	I	A	F	S	Q
P	Q	S	I	L	E	N	T	R	Z

Answer on page 110

33

Loopy Lights

John and Sarah have spent a long time decorating their Christmas tree and they love the way it looks. All that's missing are the lights. But when the twins took them out of the box, they were all knotted up and in a muddle. Can you help to untangle them by unscrambling the letters in the lights below to spell out the gift that was given on the eleventh day in the famous song, *The Twelve Days of Christmas*? When you think you've worked it out, write the letters in the right order in the lights on the opposite page.

Answer on page 110

Jesus First (1)

Christmas is meant to be a celebration of the birth of Jesus, the Son of God, here on earth. But during the run-up to Christmas Day there's loads of hustle and bustle, shopping and planning, Christmas card-writing and present-wrapping, excitement and general busyness – not to mention the sleepless nights! And it all takes up our time. So even when we love Jesus, it can be hard to remember to give Him the top spot.

We've made a list of some of the things you can do to help you keep Jesus at Number One in your life – and not just at Christmas, but all the year round. God sent His Son into the world to save us – to show us how to be close to Him and live our lives the way He wants us to. The wrong things we sometimes do can make a bit of a mess of our friendship with God, but when we say sorry and give our lives to Jesus, we can be friends with Him again. Isn't that the best news ever for a really happy Christmas!

Here are Dave and Benny's ideas to help you keep Jesus where He belongs in your life – in the top spot:

1. When you wake up in the morning, before you do anything else, say thank You to Jesus for the brand-new day. Even if it's pouring with rain or freezing cold, it's still a day to be thankful for.

2. Read your Bible every day. It helps you to get to know Jesus and to discover all about God's love for you.

3. Learn some verses from the Bible by heart. It's very helpful to have little bits in your head to remind you how special you are to Jesus. If you don't already know them, try learning these:

   'And I will be with you always, to the end of the age' (Jesus' words from Matthew 28 verse 20).

   'Do not be worried and upset; do not be afraid' (Jesus' words from John 14 verse 27).

4. Spend time talking to Jesus. Tell Him how you're feeling and thank Him for the good things in your life. Remember to listen to Jesus, too. He may have something important to say to you.

5. Go to church regularly if you can. Jesus loves it when we meet up with other Christians and we can learn about Him and enjoy worshipping Him all together.

Jesus First (2):
Mary at Jesus' Feet

In the Bible, the book of Luke – chapter 10 and verses 38 to 42 – tells of the time Jesus visited two sisters called Martha and Mary. Read the story and, in ALL the pictures, draw Mary sitting on the floor in front of Jesus and listening to Him.

When Jesus visited Martha and Mary, Martha was very busy. But Mary stopped what she was doing straight away so that she could listen to Jesus' teaching.

Mary listened and listened.

'It's not fair!' Martha complained. 'There's so much work to do and Mary's doing nothing. Jesus, tell her to help me!'

But Jesus said, 'Martha, stop worrying about everything! Mary has chosen to do the right thing by sitting still and listening to me. I'm not going to stop her.'

Mary was right to give Jesus her undivided attention. We all have lots to do. We can be very busy with work and play. But at some point every day, just like Mary, it's important to give Jesus our undivided attention, too.

Christmas Around the World

You obviously know that, where Christmas is celebrated around the world, it's always on 25 December. But did you also know that, for some countries of the world, the Christmas season falls in the winter, and for others, it falls in the summer? This is because the globe of the earth is in two halves. One half is called the NORTHERN HEMISPHERE and the other half is called the SOUTHERN HEMISPHERE.

The earth is constantly travelling around the sun. Because of the way the earth is tilted, this means that from September to March, the Northern Hemisphere is further away from the sun, making the weather colder and bringing on the winter. However, it also means that, at the same time, the Southern Hemisphere is closer to the sun, so that the weather there is warmer and it becomes summer.

Continents in the Northern Hemisphere include Europe, North and Central America, and most of Asia. The UK is in the Northern Hemisphere, too.

Continents in the Southern Hemisphere include Australia, New Zealand, South America and Southern Africa.

Wherever You Live ...

1. What do you like to wear when the weather is hot?

_____

2. What do you like to wear when the weather is cold?

_____

3. What's your favourite summer weather food?

_____

4. What's your favourite winter weather food?

_____

5. What outdoor fun do you like to have on sunny, summer days?

_____

6. How would you rather spend your time on cold, wintry days?

41

More Seasonal Stuff

1. Which three months of the year do we call 'winter'?

_____   _____   _____

2. What do hedgehogs do all winter long?

☐ Eat   ☐ Read a lot

☐ Sleep   ☐ Go away to a warmer country

3. Why do lorries spread salt on wintry roads?

☐ It gets rid of excess salt

☐ Snails like the taste

☐ It soaks up rain

☐ It melts ice

4. Where does a squirrel spend most of the winter?

☐ In a bush   ☐ In a bird box

☐ In a hotel   ☐ In a drey

5. What does a badger do in winter?

☐ Same as it does all year round

☐ Wear thick socks   ☐ Go to sleep

☐ Climb up trees to find shelter

6. What's the name for trees that lose their leaves in winter?

☐ Decimal   ☐ Deciduous

☐ Decomposed   ☐ Eric

7. Where do swallows fly to spend the winter?

☐ Africa ☐ Australia ☐ It's a secret ☐ Austria

8. How many sides does a snowflake have?

☐ Six ☐ Three ☐ Eight ☐ It's round

9. What is a 'blizzard'?

☐ A baby lizard   ☐ A thunder storm

☐ Heavy rain and wind   ☐ Heavy snow and wind

Did you know ...?
The world's tallest snowman was built in Bethel in Maine, USA, in 2008. It stood a whopping 37 metres and its arms were made of trees!

Still being Seasonal ...

10. Where can you sometimes find frogs in winter?

☐ On river banks   ☐ Buried in mud in ponds

☐ In garden sheds   ☐ Under the sofa

11. What's the name for trees that keep their greenery through the winter and the rest of the year?

☐ Ever ready   ☐ Evil

☐ Everlasting   ☐ Evergreen

12. What do squirrels feed on mostly through the winter?

☐ Acorns   ☐ Mushrooms

☐ Nut roast   ☐ Conkers

13. What is black ice?

☐ Ice that's dirty from being on the ground

☐ Ice-covered blackcurrants

☐ Ice that's very hard to see

☐ Ice that only forms at night

14. What are 'snowdrops'?

☐ Baby teeth   ☐ Flowers

☐ Snowflakes   ☐ Sweets

15. On very cold, winter mornings, what do you sometimes see covering grass and plants on the ground?

☐ Dust   ☐ Seeds   ☐ Icing sugar   ☐ Frost

16. Which of these occurs in the winter?

☐ Longest day of the year

☐ Two Thursdays in the same week

☐ Shortest day of the year

17. Snowflakes are always the same shape.

☐ True   ☐ False   ☐ Depends where they land

18. Where do snowflakes form?

☐ In the fridge   ☐ In the air

☐ In the clouds   ☐ On the ground

Answers on page 110

Josie's Present Problem

Josie's finally decided what Christmas presents she's going to buy for her mum and her dad. She wants to give her mum a new hat and her dad a new tie. But there are so many hats and ties to choose from that she can't make up her mind. Can you help?

Here are some pictures of Josie's mum. Draw a different hat on each one so that Josie can decide which type of hat will suit her mum best.

Can you help Josie to choose a tie for her dad, too? Here are some pictures showing him wearing a tie. Colour each tie differently – either use blocks of colour or create patterns – so that Josie can work out what sort of tie will make her dad look smartest.

Did You Know ...?

The Topz Gang has been investigating Christmas and has uncovered a load of funky facts!

- Traditionally, we think of THREE wise men visiting Jesus, but in fact the Bible doesn't say how many there were. Perhaps the idea of three men comes from the three gifts they brought with them that *are* mentioned in the Bible – gold, frankincense and myrrh.

- God had a reason for wanting His Son to be called Jesus. The name means 'God saves'. God sent Jesus to earth to save people from their sins (the wrong things that we all sometimes do) and to show them how to be friends with God again.

- Do you think there's an innkeeper in the Christmas story as it's told in the Bible? Well, guess what? There isn't! Luke simply writes in his Gospel that there was no room for Mary and Joseph in the inn.

- Joseph had a very important ancestor (someone who was part of his family a long, long time ago). He was a king called David.

- An old man called Simeon, who loved God, knew that God was sending Someone special to save people and to show them how to be close to Him again. Because Simeon had been waiting for this special Someone for so long, God promised him that he would not die before he had seen Jesus. God told Simeon to go to the temple – and that's where he met the young Jesus, when Mary and Joseph took Him there to dedicate Him to God. God kept His promise to Simeon.

- A man called Herod was the king when Jesus was born. When Herod heard about the birth of Jesus – the new King – he wanted Him dead. But he couldn't find Jesus, so he did something really terrible. He ordered that ALL the baby boys of two years old and under, living in the area, should be killed. He didn't want Jesus to escape.

- King Herod wasn't a nice man. He murdered lots of other people, too, including some of his own family.

And Did You Know That On Christmas Day ...?

- In 1066, famous king of England, William the Conqueror, was crowned at Westminster Abbey in London.

- In 1642, Sir Isaac Newton was born. He was a very clever and famous scientist.

- In 1818, the Christmas carol, 'Silent Night, Holy Night', was sung for the very first time in a church in Austria. The words were written by an Austrian priest, in the Austrian language, and they form the oldest known Christmas carol in the world.

- In 1914, during the First World War, something like 100,000 British and German soldiers stopped fighting for the day. They met up with each other and sang carols together. Some of them even played soccer!

- In 1932, King George V's chair collapsed while he was giving a speech at Christmas dinner!

- In 1939, Charles Dickens' famous story, *A Christmas Carol*, was broadcast on the radio for the first time.

- In 1952, Queen Elizabeth II gave her first Christmas speech. It was broadcast on the radio, and not on television, as not everyone had a television in their home back then.

- In 1990, the Internet was tested for the very first time! It's hard to believe that the world used to manage without the Internet but – yes, it did!!

And guess what? The very first time that Christmas was DEFINITELY celebrated on 25 December was all the way back in the year 352!

Boxing Day BIG Topz 20

I think Christmas is super-cool! All of it – the days leading up to THE BIG DAY, *and* the ones that come afterwards. I hardly sleep at all on Christmas Eve, and then on Christmas Day I'm too excited to feel tired! But if your Christmas has been really full-on and supercharged, sometimes Boxing Day can feel a little bit quiet with not much going on. That's when you need a bunch of stuff up your sleeve to keep you busy and help the Christmas feeling to last on and on! Here are ten of my Topz Boxing Day tips. Try and come up with another ten ideas of your own and then you'll have a handy Boxing Day Topz twenty all ready for the next time you need some Boxing Day inspiration.

1. Enjoy playing the games and having a proper look at the books and other stuff that you've (hopefully!) been given for Christmas. (Sometimes you don't look at them properly on Christmas Day because you're so busy being excited!)

2. Go for a run round the park – or even round and round the garden, important after all that Christmas pudding. (I usually have two helpings – with custard and ice cream!!)

3. Text or email friends and find out what presents they got for Christmas. You could make this into a guessing game and give each other clues.

4. Make a play list of films you have on DVD that you could watch with your family – then start watching them.

5. Look through your Christmas Day family photos – hopefully you'll have some – and try to come up with a funny caption for each one. Then see if you can make your family laugh!

6. Test your family's knowledge about Christmas with the Christmas quizzes in this book.

7. Pick some cool music and make up a Boxing Day dance – then teach it to everyone else in the house! (They might need persuading, but you'll figure it out!)

8. Make a Christmas present list for your friends and family for NEXT year! Saves time next December!!

9. Write a diary or blog about the Christmas Day you've just had. Should be fun to read at Christmas next year.

10. Make some New Year greetings cards to give to your friends and family to wish them happy days over the next twelve months.

More for a Boxing Day Big Topz 20!

So, now you've read Danny's Topz ten ideas – is your brain in gear? Write down YOUR ten tips for a Topz Boxing Day here!

11 _____

_____

12 _____

_____

13 _____

_____

14 _____

_____

15 _____

_____

16

17

18

19

20

Your Boxing Day sounds Topz!

Topz 10 Definitely NOTs!

Having lots of things to do is great. I love it when there's loads going on – especially in the school holidays. As long as it's fun stuff, that is. Sometimes Mum asks me to tidy my room and, to be honest, I'd rather have nothing to do at all than tidying! Bleeaargh! But if you ever do get bored – and I hope it's not often – here's a list of things you should DEFINITELY NOT do! Why not add five NOTs of your own to make a tidy Topz ten!

1. DON'T cut the bottoms off your pyjama trousers to make them into swimming trunks to wear the next time you have a bath.

2. DON'T hide someone's glasses (speccy type) under the cushions on the sofa.

3. DON'T take ALL the books out of ALL the bookcases in your house to build a den.

4. DON'T hide behind a door and leap out shouting 'Boo!' at someone who is carrying a tray full of china.

5. DON'T EVER dig a big hole in the garden and wait for someone to fall in it. (NOT EVER, you hear me??)

Time for you to come up with five of your DEFINITELY NOTS – and DEFINITELY means **DEFINITELY!!**

6 _____

_____

7 _____

_____

8 _____

_____

9 _____

_____

10 _____

_____

Cool! Thanks! Now I know what I DEFINITELY WON'T be doing the next time I'm bored!!

Topz Presents for Topz Pets!

Sarah and John have some brilliant present ideas for their pets.

On Sarah's list for her cat, Saucy, are:

A box of cat treats
A snugly cushion
A soft toy mouse
A scratching post

On John's list for his dog, Gruff, are:

A ball
A box of biscuits
A chewy bone
A blanket

Can you think of anything else that would make good Christmas presents for Gruff and Saucy? Write your ideas down here:

People keep all sorts of animals as pets. Look at the pets listed here and write down next to them your idea for a fun – and suitable – Christmas present.

Hamster

Guinea pig

Horse

Lizard

Rabbit

Snake

Mouse

Tarantula

Goldfish

Goat

Rat

Tortoise

Chinchilla

Prayers at Christmas

For me and my family, and for my friends in the Topz Gang, Christmas is a brilliant time! I *really* hope it is for you, too. But for some, it can be lonely, sad, and hard to get through. There are people who have nowhere to live and not enough food to eat. There are others who are all alone. Sarah and John's next door neighbour, Mrs Allbright, has lived on her own since her husband died, and she misses him a lot. Last Christmas, Sarah asked everyone in Sunday Club if they could pray for her. She wanted God to be close to Mrs Allbright. She wanted her to know how much God loves her – especially at Christmas when it's easy to feel forgotten, with everyone around you enjoying themselves.

Do you know anyone who might be lonely and sad, or hungry and with nowhere to live at Christmas? Even if you don't, you can be sure that there are many people who need to know God's love and care every day, and perhaps in particular at this time of year. Why not write a short prayer for them here – then you can say it to God every day over Christmas time.

'I am with you ...'

Jesus, the Son of God, has promised to be close to each
one of us when we ask Him to be. Draw Jesus standing
next to the people in each of the pictures below to
remind you that whatever happens, we are never alone.
As you draw each figure of Jesus, ask Him to be close to
anyone who is lonely, or sick, or homeless, or sad and
pray that they will come to know His love.

Panto Time! (1)

Not only is Christmas a time for fun, family and festivities, in theatres all over Britain it's also pantomime time! Lots of you will probably have seen a pantomime at some time or another, but in case you haven't, a pantomime is a stage show that tells the story of a popular fairytale. It might be *The Sleeping Beauty*, or *Cinderella* – or any one of loads of other well-known stories.

It's a tradition of pantomime that the main boy character is actually played by a girl, and is known as 'the principal boy', and one of the main female characters (perhaps the mother of the boy) is played by a man, and is known as 'the dame'. I know! Crazy! There is always an evil baddie, lots of jokes and singing and dancing – and every single ending is a happy-ever-after.

How about putting on a pantomime in your own home just for your family, and starring you, your friends or your brothers and sisters (as long as they want to join in, too!). Or, you could use any toys you have to play all the parts, like a puppet show. You could turn a table into a stage by covering it with a sheet, and hiding behind it while you make the toys act out the show on the tabletop.

Ready? Then it's time to get Panto Planning!

First of all, you need a story. Think of as many fairytales as you can that you know well. Go through the plots in your head (or read them in a fairytale book if you have one) to see how easy they would be to act out pantomime-style, and how many characters each one might need. Then choose ONE!

Here's a list of a few fairytales to get you started and help you to decide:

Snow White and the Seven Dwarfs (big cast of characters needed for this one)

Beauty and the Beast (Josie's favourite)

Goldilocks and the Three Bears (Benny's favourite because he loves porridge)

The Babes in the Wood

Puss in Boots

Little Red Riding Hood (Paul's favourite because, if he could play the wolf, his glasses would be perfect when he was disguised as Red Riding Hood's grandmother)

Jack and the Beanstalk

Aladdin (not exactly a fairytale, but makes a very popular pantomime)

Panto Time! (2)

Have you decided which story your pantomime is going to tell? If so, write the title here:

_____

Who are the different characters from the story who will appear in your pantomime? Write them here and remember to make sure that you have enough people or toys to play all the parts – or you could play more than one character, but obviously not in the same scene!

_____

_____

_____

_____

_____

_____

Which part would you like to play?

_____

Now for the Script!

Now's the time to read your pantomime story through carefully to make sure you know it really well. Use the space below to write down the main events that happen, so that you know how many different scenes your pantomime might need and which part of the story each scene will tell.

_____

_____

_____

_____

_____

_____

_____

_____

_____

_____

_____

All done? Phew!!

Panto Time! (3)

When it comes to **setting the scene**, you probably won't have the space or the materials to be big and grand like on a theatre stage – with castles and palaces and dark, creepy forests! But it doesn't matter! This is about creating your VERY OWN PANTOMIME in your VERY OWN HOME, so using what's there will be just as effective, for example chairs and tables and cushions. And you can use them in different ways. A cushion could become a magical coach drawn by two chairs as the horses, for instance.

However, the less you have to move things around, the better. You can simply make an announcement before a scene starts so that the audience know where it's supposed to be – for example: 'In the palace kitchen' or 'At the top of the beanstalk' or 'In the ballroom'.

You can also do this for a 'puppet' panto with toys on a tabletop. Then there's no need to make mini-scenery – unless of course you want to! As long as your audience is sitting comfortably and everyone has a good view, then their imaginations (and yours!) can fill in the rest.

Panto Props

What would be helpful is to have a few props. Props (short for 'properties') are the things actors use on the stage. For example, if Cinderella is in the kitchen cooking, it would be useful for her to have a saucepan and a wooden spoon. Or if Snow White is cleaning the dwarves' cottage, she needs a duster.

Go through your story and see what simple props the characters might need. Then make a list of them here.

_____

_____

_____

_____

_____

_____

_____

_____

_____

_____

_____

Panto Time! (4)

This is a REALLY fun bit! Your pantomime characters all need **costumes**. Even toys in a 'puppet' panto are going to need dressing up. But again, just as with the scenery, you can keep things very simple.

You and your co-stars may already have clothes that would be perfect for the parts you are all playing. If not, scarves, shawls, towels and even sheets can be wrapped around or draped over what you're wearing to give you a different look. Creating costumes like this also means you can change quickly if you need to for a different scene.

Scarves are especially good for toys, too. And if you have any hats, as long as they are right for the character, these are also a brilliant and quick way to help you to create the look of the person you're playing. How about a pair of sunglasses for a cool dude prince!

There's space opposite to write down the kind of costumes each character in your panto will need. Include notes about how you could put them together if you're using scarves, towels and sheets. Don't forget, if you're borrowing anything from someone else, always ask first.

Panto Time! (5)

Now you're ready to start **rehearsing**! You don't need a complicated script. Just call your co-stars (or your toys!) together and agree which parts you're all going to play.

Then, using the scene notes you made earlier, tell the story to your cast (the actors in your panto). To help them get to know it, you could try telling it two or three times and then ask everyone to tell the whole story again between them, with each person saying a few sentences each.

Once you all know the story well, you can begin to 'improvise' the scenes. 'Improvising' is a word used by actors for making it up as you go along! Start by thinking about the scenes in your pantomime one by one, and then imagine the conversations the different characters might have.

Here's an example to help you get started.

In *Jack and the Beanstalk*, Jack's mum sends him to market to sell their cow because they are very poor and need the money. But instead of money, Jack comes back with just a handful of beans. His conversation with his mum might go like this:

Mum: How much money did you get for our cow?

Jack: Well … erm … I didn't actually get any money. But I did get some *brilliant* beans!

Mum: (Angrily) Beans? What good are beans to us? We need money, you stupid boy! Now we still haven't got any money and we haven't got a cow either!

Jack: No, Mum, you don't understand. These are *magic* beans!

Mum: (Pretending to be pleased) Oh, *are* they?

Jack: (Smiling) Yes, they are!

Mum: (Angry again) If those beans are magic, then I'm the Queen of England!

Jack: (Surprised) Are you?

Mum: No!

Get the idea? Just think about *who* your characters are and how they might speak, and start to get a conversation going like that. If anyone says something that you think is especially good or funny, you could write it down so that you all remember it, but there's no need to write down the whole script unless you want to. You can just keep rehearsing each scene until everyone is completely sure of what they're doing. And then …

Time to put it all together!

Panto Time! (6)

So this is it! There's just one more thing to do. Design a programme for your audience! When you go to the theatre to see a show, there are booklets that tell you who is playing which part (the cast list), and perhaps a little bit about the show itself, too. This is the 'programme'. For yours, you only need one piece of paper: on the front, put the panto title and draw a picture – perhaps a character or a scene from the pantomime. On the back, you could write a short paragraph saying what the panto is about, and underneath put your cast list.

Use the space below to plan the back of your programme, and on the page opposite, practise drawing a funky-looking cover. When you know exactly what you want to appear on your programme, copy the whole thing onto a piece of paper ready to give to your audience!

_____

_____

_____

_____

_____

_____

_____

Design your Perfect Panto Programme cover here!

So … you've chosen your pantomime, sorted out your acting area, put together some funky costumes and rehearsed till you know what you're doing inside out and back to front! And now …

IT'S PANTO TIME!

How Well Do You Know Your Fairytales?

While you're in the panto mood, try this quirky quiz to see how well you know what goes on in fairytale land!

1. Snow White's stepmother was very …?

[ ] tall   [ ] kind   [ ] beautiful

2. The Pied Piper said that he could get rid of the plague of rats in …?

[ ] Hull   [ ] Hamelin   [ ] Hornchurch

3. Rapunzel had very long …?

[ ] ears   [ ] hair   [ ] toe nails

4. In her spell, the wicked fairy said that the Sleeping Beauty would die when she was …?

[ ] sixteen   [ ] eighteen   [ ] twenty-one

5. Little Red Riding Hood's mother sent her into the woods with a basket of goodies to ...?

☐ have a picnic

☐ give to her uncle, the woodcutter

☐ take to her grandmother who was ill

6. When Hansel and Gretel were lost in the woods, they found a house made of ...?

☐ gingerbread   ☐ straw   ☐ Lego

7. In the giant's castle at the top of the beanstalk, Jack found ...?

☐ a lamb with a golden fleece

☐ a hen that laid golden eggs

☐ a lion with a golden mane

8. When the three bears returned to their cottage in the woods, they found Goldilocks ...?

☐ eating their porridge   ☐ watching television

☐ asleep in baby bear's bed

More Fairytale Fun!

9. The princess kissed the frog and he turned into …?

☐ a prince ☐ a llama ☐ a cat

10. When the fairies gave a thumb-sized baby to an elderly couple, the couple called him …?

☐ George ☐ Tom ☐ Henry

11. The Sleeping Beauty pricked her finger on …?

☐ a hedgehog ☐ a rose bush

☐ a spinning wheel

12. Snow White's stepmother asked the magic mirror, 'Mirror, mirror, on the wall, who is the …?'

☐ fairest of them all ☐ oldest of them all

☐ happiest of them all

13. The prince got into Rapunzel's tower by …?

☐ climbing a ladder ☐ pole vaulting

☐ climbing Rapunzel's hair

14. Before he grew up, the beautiful swan thought he was …?

☐ an angel   ☐ a seagull

☐ an ugly duckling

15. When the people wouldn't pay the Pied Piper what they owed him for getting rid of the rats, he took their …?

☐ goats   ☐ children   ☐ queen

16. In her grandmother's cottage, Little Red Riding Hood found the wolf disguised as …?

☐ the wood cutter   ☐ her grandmother

☐ the prime minister

Answers on page 110

Topz Christmas Surprises!

Dave's come up with a cool list of Christmas presents for his mum and dad and his friends in the Topz Gang. But it's a secret so he's written each gift backwards and in code. Can you crack the code, then turn the back-to-front words the right way round to find out what gifts Dave's going to give? (It's all right – you're allowed to know!)

1. = a   ?1 = b   2. = c   ?2 = d   3. = e   ?3 = f   etc

Mum   ?9 5. 1. ?4   ?9 3. 13. ?9 ?2
Uncrack   __ __ __ __   __ __ __ __ __
Turn around __ __ __ __   __ __ __ __ __

Dad   ?9 8. ?10 1. ?6 11. 2. ?6 1. 2.
Uncrack   __ __ __ __ __ __ __ __ __ __
Turn around __ __ __ __ __ __ __ __ __ __

John   ?10 ?6 3. ?3   10. ?7 3. ?8
Uncrack   __ __ __ __   __ __ __ __
Turn around __ __ __ __   __ __ __ __

Sarah   10. 3. ?10 1. ?6 8. 2. 8. ?4 2.
Uncrack   __ __ __ __ __ __ __ __ __ __
Turn around __ __ __ __ __ __ __ __ __ __

Benny   3. ?6 ?13 ?13 11. ?8   6. 8. 8. ?1
Uncrack   __ __ __ __ __ __   __ __ __ __
Turn around __ __ __ __ __ __   __ __ __ __

78

Danny	?6 ?6 1. ?1 ?10 8. 8. ?3 10. 6. 2. 8. 10.
Uncrack	__ __ __ __ __ __ __ __ __ __ __ __
Turn around	__ __ __ __ __ __ __ __ __ __ __ __

Josie	10. 3. ?11 8. ?6 4.
Uncrack	__ __ __ __ __ __
Turn around	__ __ __ __ __ __

Paul	4. ?7 5. 13. 1. ?6 ?8 10. ?2 ?9 1. 2.
Uncrack	__ __ __ __ __ __ __ __ __ __ __ __
Turn around	__ __ __ __ __ __ __ __ __ __ __ __

Have you worked them all out? **(Answers on page 111.)** Now try and find them in the word search.

G	S	M	G	S	J	X	M	H	G	P	P	F	V	V
K	F	O	O	T	B	A	L	L	S	O	C	K	S	I
G	O	G	C	K	I	F	O	V	N	P	O	D	C	C
F	U	U	S	W	J	V	S	D	U	O	R	R	Y	H
C	O	L	Z	R	E	K	Y	M	B	A	E	G	Z	O
A	W	Q	P	S	P	J	Z	E	C	Y	U	O	N	C
J	J	V	U	C	U	N	L	G	R	B	H	S	A	O
T	T	Q	S	F	S	Z	N	D	E	M	L	L	R	L
N	L	H	K	V	Z	I	R	O	C	Y	C	N	A	A
I	A	R	J	U	Y	I	J	M	T	U	D	P	V	T
O	T	D	P	A	A	R	E	F	L	L	F	M	F	E
D	D	B	L	H	T	U	E	A	E	B	E	D	M	S
Y	C	P	Z	Q	L	L	T	A	R	Q	U	U	G	K
W	Q	W	K	K	T	O	U	Z	C	M	A	S	P	B
E	P	E	N	S	R	A	Z	H	K	K	B	H	N	B

Answer on page 111

All God's Gifts

It's not just people who enjoy giving presents. On the very first Christmas, God showed how much He loves us by giving us the greatest gift of all: His Son, Jesus.

Jesus lived with us here on earth for thirty-three years. He showed God's love to so many people. He taught us how God wants us to live our lives. He promised us that if we believe that He is God's Son and say sorry for the wrong things we do that can spoil our friendship with God, then we can be with our Father God FOREVER.

But when Jesus went back to heaven after those thirty-three years, God didn't leave us on our own. He sent us *another* gift: His Holy Spirit, who came to live inside us and to help us to stay close to God every day. God's Spirit is always there ready to listen to us when we need Him. He is our Friend and we can talk to Him just as we talk to our other friends.

In the Bible, there are two letters from a man called Paul to his friend, Timothy. Paul wrote to Timothy about the Holy Spirit:

'For the Spirit that God has given us does not make us timid; instead, his Spirit fills us with power, love, and self-control'(2 Timothy 1 verse 7).

When we believe in Jesus, God's Spirit is with us every single moment. What an amazing present!

And God doesn't just give gifts to us at Christmas. He goes on giving them day after day – all year round – and year after year!

Make a list here of all the good things in your life – for example, your friends, the people who love you, the place where you live. Think of as many good things as you can – and then say a HUGE thank You to God for giving you such wonderful presents!

_____

_____

_____

_____

_____

_____

_____

_____

_____

_____

_____

THANK YOU, FATHER GOD!

What can YOU give to God?

I don't know about you, but I seem to spend quite a bit of my prayer times *asking* God for different things. If I'm not well, I ask Him to help me feel better. If I'm worried about something, I ask Him to stay close to me and help me. Sometimes I even ask Him to help me with my homework! But God is my Friend – my very best Friend – and it's important to remember to *give* to Him, not just to *ask* of Him.

- Josie gives God her love by praising and trying to obey Him.

- She gives Him her time by talking and listening to Him, and by trying to help other people just as Jesus would have done.

- She also gives some of her pocket money to her church to help with the work it does, and sometimes buys tins of food for Greg, the youth leader, to take to the homeless shelter. All these are ways of giving to God.

Why not think about some ways that YOU could give to God? Write your ideas down here. It doesn't matter if some of your gifts are the same as Josie's.

_____

_____

_____

_____

_____

_____

_____

_____

_____

_____

_____

_____

_____

God loves what we give when we give to Him with love.

What the Widow Gave

The Gospel of Mark in the New Testament tells this story of a poor widow (Mark 12 verses 41 to 44).

Draw the right amount of coins in each picture.

Draw lots and lots of coins pouring out of the rich man's bag.

As Jesus sat in the Temple one day, he watched people dropping money into the collection box. Lots of rich people came to the Temple and they left lots of money.

Then a poor widow arrived and dropped just two small coins into the box.

Draw in two coins dropping from the widow's hand.

Jesus said to His special friends, the disciples, 'This woman has given more than all the others. They have plenty but gave only the money they had to spare. This woman is poor – and she has given everything she has'.

God loves you so much. How can you give Him a special gift today?

The Topz Gang's Topz Christmas Moments

Sometimes things happen that are so funny or so brilliant that you never want to forget them. It might be something you can capture on a camera or mobile phone, or just something someone says or does that you want to remember forever.

The Topz Gang have each got their own favourite Topz Christmas moment. Here they are:

When Mum and Dad and I were so busy playing the new game of Scrabble I'd given them, that we forgot to cook our Christmas lunch!

When Mum and Dad told me that we were all going on holiday to Australia as a family Christmas present!

On Christmas Eve when Gruff first saw the snowmen we'd built in the garden. He must have thought they were burglars because he went mad at them!

When Dad went up to the loft to get the Christmas tree down and found a sleeping bat!

When I opened my Christmas card from my cousin, Gabby, and inside she'd written: 'Merry Christmas, Josie! It's very cool having you and Sarah as my best friends. xx'

On Christmas morning when Dad opened my present to him and he said it was the best present in the whole world ever! I gave him a Bible.

When I woke up on Boxing (Day) Night because I had a nightmare, and Mum went downstairs with me and we sat in the kitchen eating chocolate till really late!

What about you? Have you got a Topz Christmas Moment? Write it down here so that you can remember it forever!

_____

_____

_____

_____

_____

Snowmen Spot the Difference

It's snowed in Holly Hill! John, Sarah and Josie have lost no time in building a snowman in the twins' garden. In fact there was enough snow for them to build *four* snowmen!

They tried to make the snowmen all look the same, but in the end one of them was a bit different. Can you see how? There are five differences altogether.

Answers on page 111

What's in the Dots?

Paul loves playing in the snow, too, but he didn't want to make a snow*man*. Join the dots to find out what Paul decided to build out of snow instead!

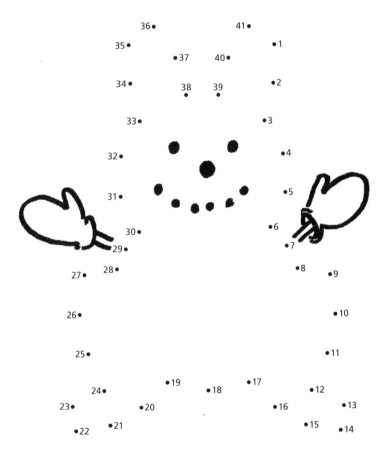

Crazy Christmas!

Here are some quirky questions from your friends in the Topz Gang to find out what would make your CRAZIEST Christmas ever!

1. What would be the craziest Christmas present to receive?

_____

_____

2. What would be the craziest Christmas present to give and who would be the craziest person to give it to?

_____

_____

3. What would be the craziest topping to serve with a mince pie?

_____

_____

4. What would be the craziest picture to put on a Christmas card?

_____

_____

7. What would be the craziest Christmas clothes to wear?

_____

_____

8. What would be the craziest decoration to hang on a Christmas tree?

_____

_____

9. What would be the craziest thing to find inside a Christmas cracker?

_____

_____

10. What would be the craziest Christmas game to play?

_____

_____

11. Who would be the craziest person to turn up on your doorstep for Christmas lunch?

_____

_____

Wow! Now that's wacky!

The Names of Jesus

Jesus Christ is the most special and important Person ever to have been born into our world. He is the Son of God – and you can't get any more special and important than that!

So perhaps it's not surprising that the Bible tells us that Jesus was known by many different names.

As well as 'Jesus', He is called:

- Immanuel
- Christ
- Messiah

In the Old Testament, in the book of Isaiah, the birth of Jesus is actually announced – but lots and lots of years before it happened! A good SEVEN HUNDRED years in fact!!

This is called 'a prophecy', and in chapter 9 and verse 6 of his book, the prophet Isaiah gives us some more names for Jesus.

Here they are – and they're awesome!

Colour them in and decorate them with patterns. Make them look as awesome as they sound!

Wonderful Counsellor

Mighty God

Eternal Father

Prince of Peace

What brilliant designs for homemade Christmas cards!

Happy Recycled Christmas!

Did you know ...?

Every year in Britain, well over ONE BILLION Christmas cards are bought, written out and sent to friends and family!

A billion is a pretty big number to imagine, so it might help you to think of it as ONE THOUSAND MILLION (because that's the same as one billion).

In figures, one billion looks like this: 1,000,000,000

Look at all those zeros! Loads of them! So well over ONE BILLION Christmas cards is a *serious* amount of Christmas greetings!

And guess what else ...?

In order to make more than one billion Christmas cards, a massive TWO HUNDRED THOUSAND – that's 200,000 – trees have to be cut down!

Not only that, but we wrap up presents with roughly an astonishing EIGHT THOUSAND (8,000) TONS of wrapping paper made from another FIFTY THOUSAND (50,000) trees!

And that's JUST in the UK – let alone all around the world!

It can't be right simply to throw ALL those cards and ALL that wrapping paper (which actually means ALL THOSE TREES) away.

So, here are some Topz tips for rubbish to help you cut right down on Christmas waste:

1. You can put all your cards into your family's recycling bin – or some supermarkets collect them for charities who turn them into things like newspapers and paper towels. Some charities will then use the money raised to plant new trees.

2. Cut off the back halves of your Christmas cards – ie the part that's been written on by the sender. Keep any special messages if you want to. Otherwise recycle the unwanted bits of card as in no. 1. You can then put the picture halves away to re-use (recycle) next Christmas, when you could cut out images from the pictures to make labels for presents. Or you could use scissors to cut wavy edges around the whole pictures to make 'new' Christmas cards to send. That way your cards can be used twice before ending up in the recycling bin.

3. Unwrapping presents is very exciting, but if you can manage to unwrap them carefully, then you shouldn't damage the paper too much. It can then be folded up and put away to be used again next Christmas. If you do need to throw some away, as with the cards, pop it in your recycling bin.

Have fun recycling!

New Year Topz 20

Exactly a week after Christmas, a brand-new year arrives. Whoop-whoop! Something else to celebrate! And at the start of each new year, lots of people like to make 'resolutions'. They decide on a whole bunch of things they're going to do through the year and try to stick to them. Quite common resolutions include things like getting more exercise or eating less chocolate. Well, in the Topz Gang, we like to think of them as New Year challenges rather than New Year resolutions, and this year we've decided to have a crack at two challenges each! Here's what we've come up with to do. Do you think these challenges are going to be easy or hard for whichever one of us is planning to do them? As you read them, put an 'e' for easy or an 'h' for hard in the box after each one.

1. Go on a cycling holiday – a proper one, where you cycle for miles and take a tent with you to camp in at night.

☐

2. Beat Danny in a cycling race (because I *never* can).

☐

3. Eat a crisp, cornflake, hard-boiled egg and Marmite sandwich (after all, this is ME we're talking about!).

☐

4. Score at least two goals in at least eight football matches.

☐

5. Learn how to make a raspberry pavlova (the most yumptious pudding in the history of the world and all its yumptious puddings – crispy meringue with loads of cream and piles of raspberries!!).

☐

6. Learn how to put up a shelf (which will make Dad very happy).

☐

7. Spend more time playing football with Josie.

☐

8. Train Saucy not to eat Gruff's food (makes John cross – not to mention Gruff!).

☐

New Year Topz 20 (continued)

9. Get up early and go and run round the park at least four times a week whether I feel like it or not.

☐

10. Save up my pocket money to get some really cool lights for my bike (those flashy ones – they're awesome!).

☐

11. Don't argue so much with Sarah – could be tricky because I see she hasn't put 'Don't argue so much with John' as one of her challenges.

☐

12. Train Gruff not to eat Saucy's food (makes Saucy cross and then Sarah gets in a bad mood).

☐

13. Do more violin practice so I might get into the school orchestra when I go to Bruford Secondary.

☐

14. Learn to enjoy bananas (because they're good for you).

☐

Between them, Topz have come up with FOURTEEN New Year challenges!

See if you can think up SIX more that *you'd* like to try in the New Year. Write them down here to make up an awesome TOPZ TWENTY! And don't forget to keep checking back at this list as the year goes on to see how many you've achieved. When you've completed a challenge, tick it off!

15.

16.

17.

18.

19.

20.

Wow! Take a Look at the Old Year's Highlights!

New Year's Eve is a great time to get thinking! You're right at the end of another year. Hopefully, you'll have done loads in the last twelve months, and will have plenty of awesome times to remember and make you smile!

Here's a page for you to write down your most spectacular highlights from the Old Year. Fill in which year it is, too, so that you'll always remember when it was that all these brilliant things happened.

THE YEAR

_____

_____

_____

_____

_____

_____

_____

_____

_____

Dear God, thank You for the Old …
Loving Lord, please bless the New …

New Year's Eve is also a very important time to talk to God.

• Thank and praise God for loving us and staying close to us through the Old Year.

• Ask God to bless the New Year, to watch over us, and to help us to live the way He wants us to through the next twelve months.

Think of happy times you've had and of the people you love. Think of those you know who need God's special help – and if there's anything you would like God to help you with, too. Now write a prayer to God, thanking Him and asking for His blessings on another New Year.

_____

_____

_____

_____

_____

_____

_____

Gruff and Saucy's New Year Holiday Dreams

When Christmas is over people often start to think about where they'd like to go on holiday. They decide where they're going, they book tickets and they make plans. Gruff and Saucy have their own ideas about what would make the perfect holiday.

For Saucy, the best holiday ever would involve a lot of sleeping – in a warm, comfy spot. She'd also like plenty of saucers of creamy milk.

Gruff's ideal holiday would have to be action-packed! He'd like to be somewhere where the words 'dog lead' don't exist. He'd enjoy spending all day running free across fields, snuffling through long grass, following interesting smells and going where the mood takes him. He'd also like there to be plenty of food – dog food, cat food, people food, he's really not fussy!

What about you? If you've been away on holiday before, what different places have you been to?

_____

_____

_____

_____

Which of these holidays was your favourite?

_____

Do you have a dream holiday like Gruff and Saucy? Describe it here:

_____

_____

_____

_____

_____

_____

Picture Postcards

When people go on holiday, they often send postcards to their family and friends at home. You've probably seen some arrive through your own letterbox. One side of the postcard has a photo or a drawing, and the person sending it will normally have chosen a picture that shows where they are on holiday.

On the other side, the sender will probably have written about the brilliant time they are having away.

Imagine you are away on your dream holiday! You're going to send a postcard home to let everyone know how much you're enjoying yourself. Jot down what you'd write below:

_____

_____

_____

_____

_____

_____

_____

_____

Along with your holiday news, you also want everyone to SEE your holiday place. What will the picture on your postcard be? A beach? A theme park? The campsite or hotel or cottage where you're staying?

Draw the picture on the front of your postcard here.

With tons of love from,

_____
(Sign your name)

Jesus, Light of the World

We all need light! Here's a list of some things that light up the darkness:

Lamp	Car headlamp	Candle	Moon
Glow stick	Streetlight	Stars	Fireworks
Torch	Floodlight		

See if you can find them all in the word search.

F	K	P	Q	T	H	E	U	D	Q	R	T
D	C	A	N	D	L	E	U	E	C	F	H
F	S	R	A	T	S	P	M	A	L	C	G
I	B	P	X	D	V	T	M	O	O	N	I
R	K	C	I	T	S	W	O	L	G	I	L
E	Y	G	M	C	W	D	C	R	S	U	D
W	D	S	X	P	L	M	U	A	C	T	A
O	A	Y	N	I	R	Z	Y	M	T	H	E
R	C	C	G	G	F	L	Z	Q	S	E	H
K	I	H	L	R	X	Y	F	R	C	Y	R
S	T	R	E	E	T	L	I	G	H	T	A
F	T	H	G	I	L	D	O	O	L	F	C

Answer on page 111

The celebration of Christmas is all about LIGHT.
In the book of Isaiah in the Old Testament part of the
Bible, the coming of Jesus is compared to light shining
in the dark: *'The people who walked in darkness have
seen a great light. They lived in a land of shadows, but
now light is shining on them'* (Isaiah 9 verse 2).

When God created the universe and everything in it, His
plan was that the people who lived on earth would take
care of it for Him and be His friends. But somewhere
along the way, back in Old Testament times, many of
those people turned away from God and were just
downright disobedient to Him! That meant that their
friendship with God was broken. Instead of
living in the warmth of His light, without
God's love and care people may as well
have been lost in the dark.

But that wasn't the end of it. God loves
everyone so much that He found a way
to mend things. He sent Jesus to be born
on earth and to teach people that if they
believe that He is God's Son and say sorry to
God for doing wrong things, then they can
be friends with God again forever.

On the very first Christmas, the skies over
Bethlehem were lit up as angels sang praises
to God! But the greatest Light of all time
came with the arrival of Jesus Himself. This
Light would never go out. And it wasn't just
for a stable or a street or a hillside – but for
the WHOLE, ENTIRE WORLD!

Answers

PAGE 9
Word search solution

T	U	R	K	E	Y	J	E	J	D	T	G	F	U	M	L
Z	S	Y	S	E	O	T	A	T	O	P	T	S	A	O	R
W	R	Q	H	B	V	F	G	N	I	F	F	U	T	S	U
W	C	R	O	S	T	U	N	T	S	E	H	C	P	Z	N
C	R	A	N	B	E	R	R	Y	S	A	U	C	E	W	W
D	T	S	J	S	C	S	A	T	S	U	M	A	S	T	I
G	I	E	T	V	D	E	L	S	P	I	N	S	R	A	P
F	H	T	N	D	I	G	O	L	E	L	U	Y	X	S	N
B	K	A	Z	F	L	O	P	F	C	O	K	D	G	Y	C
H	X	D	J	T	S	E	I	P	E	C	N	I	M	R	J
G	N	I	D	D	U	P	S	A	M	T	S	I	R	H	C
B	R	U	S	S	E	L	S	S	P	R	O	U	T	S	G

Wrong ingredient: Mustard

PAGES 10–11
1 Nazareth
2 Gabriel
3 False
4 King David
5 Bethlehem
6 Stable
7 Shepherds
8 True
9 Sang praises
10 False

PAGE 15
Word search solution

P	I	L	S	U	I	B	M	D	C	S
F	S	E	L	B	U	A	B	A	L	W
F	L	S	L	K	X	D	N	B	C	O
A	I	N	E	C	S	D	E	S	F	B
I	G	I	B	T	Y	M	L	Q	M	N
R	H	T	A	C	H	E	V	D	F	O
I	T	R	A	E	G	Z	G	G	I	B
E	S	N	V	N	E	I	K	Q	F	B
S	E	T	A	L	O	C	O	H	C	I
S	U	Q	A	L	G	Z	H	L	U	R

PAGE 18–19
1 The east
2 In Jerusalem
3 'Where is the baby born to be the King of the Jews?'
4 The chief priests and the teachers of the Law
5 Tell him where Jesus was
6 A star
7 God told them not to
8 To Egypt

PAGES 28–29
1 red
2a After Christmas Day
2b 26, 27, 28, 29, 30, 31 Dec and 1, 2, 3, 4, 5, 6 Jan
3 Advent
4 The Angel Gabriel
5 Epiphany
6 31
7 Yes
8 White
9 Gold Frankincense Myrrh
10 King Herod thought Jesus wanted to take away his throne and be king instead of him.

PAGE 30
Answers to which plant is which quiz

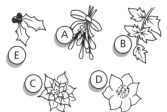

PAGE 32

1 ivy
2 royal
3 town
4 midwinter
5 nowell angel
6 Away
7 shepherds flocks
8 Silent
9 faithful
10 herald

PAGE 33

Word search solution

PAGES 35

Eleven pipers piping

PAGES 42–45

1 December January
February
2 Sleep
3 It melts ice
4 In a drey
5 Same as it does all
year round
6 Deciduous
7 Africa
8 Six

9 Heavy snow and wind
10 Buried in mud in ponds
11 Evergreen
12 Acorns
13 Ice that's very hard to see
14 Flowers
15 Frost
16 Shortest day of the year
17 False
18 In the clouds

PAGES 74–77

1 beautiful
2 Hamelin
3 hair
4 sixteen
5 take to her grandmother
who was ill
6 gingerbread
7 a hen that laid golden eggs
8 asleep in baby bear's bed
9 a prince
10 Tom
11 a spinning wheel
12 fairest of them all
13 climbing Rapunzel's hair
14 an ugly duckling
15 children
16 her grandmother

PAGES 78–79

Mum – hair dryer
Dad – calculator
John – felt pens
Sarah – chocolates
Benny – puzzle book
Danny – football socks
Josie – gloves
Paul – playing cards

Word search solution

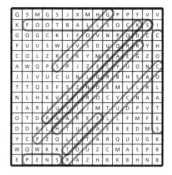

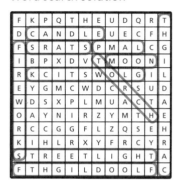

PAGE 88
Snowmen spot the difference answers

Topz is a colourful daily devotional for 7- to 11-year-olds

In each issue the Topz Gang teach children biblical truths through word games, puzzles, riddles, cartoons, competitions, simple prayers and daily Bible readings.

Available as an annual subscription (6 bimonthly issues, includes p&p) or as single issues

For current prices and more information please visit: **www.cwr.org.uk/store** call **01252 784700** or visit a Christian bookshop.